the
Writing Shed

Alan Durant has been writing poems for many
years and he thought it was about time he put them
in a book. He does most of his writing in a shed at
the bottom of his garden which is where this book
gets its title from. He has written over seventy-five
books for children of all ages – from toddlers to
teenagers – and won some prizes, including
The Royal Mail Children's Book Award in 2008.

Most of his poems and stories are based on things
that have happened to him or his children, or
things that he's really interested in or has strong
feelings about. He often visits schools and these
experiences frequently find their way into his
poems. Maybe you'll recognise someone a bit like
you or one of your friends (or one of your teachers!)
in a poem in this book. You never know...

To my family -
Jinny, Amy, Kit and Josie -
for all their inspiration, love and support.
A.D.

Some of these poems first appeared elsewhere:
Boy at the Somme (Frogs in Clogs, The Works 4),
Your Smile (Mice on Ice, The Works, Key Stage 2),
Donkeys and Stars (Look Out! The Teachers are Coming),
Letting Her Go (Why Does My Mum Always Iron a
Crease in My Jeans),
On the Beach at New Quay (A Seaside Treat)

First published in Great Britain 2010
by The Poplar Press
53 De Montfort Road, Brighton BN2 3AW

www.alandurant.co.uk
alandurant@blueyonder.co.uk

Designed and illustrated by Sue Mason
www.suemason.net

ISBN 978-0-9565-6150-3

Printed and bound in the UK
by the MPG Book Group, Bodmin and King's Lynn

Poems

from the

Writing Shed

Alan Durant

Designed and Illustrated
by Sue Mason

THE POPLAR PRESS

Contents

School Visit   6-7

Getting to School on Time   8

How Was Your Day?   9

The End   10

Creative Writing   11

What's in the Box?   12

Acrostic. Fireworks. Winter   13

Poem in Different Genres   14-15

Writing in My Shed   16

Seen Through   17

On the Beach at New Quay   18

Suncream   19

The Lie. False Impressions   20

Turning Ten   21

Georgie Porgie   22

Listen to Your Manager   23

The Carrot Eater   24

Song of the Yam. Aubergine   25

Mango. Pomegranate. Banana   26

Fruit Fantasy   27

Strawberry Madness   28-30

Ode to Custard   31

The Chocolate Monster   32-35

I Wish I Wish My Family Was Weird   36-37

I Know a Hideous Monster   38-39

Llawhaden on All Souls Night   40-41

The Dark   42

The Theme Park After Dark   43

Letting Her Go   44-45

Boy at the Somme   46

Family Plot   47

Summer's Gone   48-49

Christmas   50

Donkeys and Stars   51

Web Warning Scrabble   52

Snow Angel   53

Daybreak   54

The Metaphorical Forest   55

The Heckler   56-57

Writing Creatively   58

Haiku   59

Welcoming the New Pupils   60-61

Nursery Rhymes   62

Tic Tac Toe   63

Your Smile   64

School Visit

Mum, an orphan visited us at school today.

An orphan?

Yes, mum, you know a man that writes books.

Oh, an author. That sounds nice.

Yes it was. But James Smith was silly and pinched
Jasmine on the bottom and I had to tell Miss Harris.

What did Miss Harris say?

She said, "Not now, Naomi, you're interrupting the
story."

"Sorry," I said. Everyone was looking at me.

"May I continue now?" said the orphan.

"Yes, of course," I said. "Please do."

What was the story about?

It was about Noah's shark.

I didn't know that Noah had a shark.

Yeah, he did. He only had one though,
cause this shark ate the other one.
And then it ate the dodos too.
And now they stink.

They stink?
Yeah, there aren't
any more dodos left.
Ah, they're extinct.
Yeah they are. And then Thomas was sick on
the floor.
Right in front of the orphan. It was disgusting.
What did the author say?
He said that that he hoped it wasn't his story
That made Thomas sick.
And Phillip said, "I can see bits of carrot and
sweetcorn."
And Miss Harris said, "I don't think
We want to hear that, Phillip."
And then she put some sand on the sick.
And then the orphan said, "Does anyone want to
ask me any questions?"
And, mum, I was the first one to put my hand up.
Well done, Naomi. What did you ask?
I said, "May I be excused please?"

GETTING TO SCHOOL ON TIME:
(Twelve Top Tips)

1. Have breakfast.
2. Go to bed.
3. Sleep.
4. Wake up
5. Get out of bed
6. Get dressed
7. Grow wings.
8. Fly.
9. Don't stop at sweetshop.
10. Land in playground and fold away wings.
11. Walk into school.
    (Make sure door is open first.)
12. Racealongcorridorlikewindintoclass
    roomsitdownonchairwitharmsfolded
    ondeskreadyforregister.

Now, look up at clock and smile.

How Was Your Day?

When I get home from school at half-past three
I like to kick off my shoes, lie on the sofa and watch tv.
But my mum always nags me,
"How was school? Tell me about your day.
You never tell me anything. You never say."
So one afternoon I did. I told her about my day.
"Kenny drank his own wee just for a dare,
Michael stuck blu-tac up his nose and it got stuck there.
Andreas stuffed down four Mars Bars
and was really really sick,
Courtney wacked Xavier on the head with a stick.
Omari spat at a butterfly and hit Mr Peters in the eye.
Isabella swallowed her wobbly tooth,
Lawson threw his school bag on the roof.
Rita refused to speak, she just purred like a cat,
while Troy hung upside down from the railings
and said he was a bat.
Sanchia fell over backwards and broke the
 teacher's chair.
Olivia poured custard all over Oliver's hair.
So there you have it, Mum, there's nothing more to say.
There's nothing really to report.
It was just an ordinary day."

The End

"The world's going to end!
We're all going to die!" Tommy shouted.
"I heard it on the news.
The world's going to end!"
All that morning at school he kept on and on,
"The world's going to end!
We're all going to die!"
On and on and on...
in the classroom,
in the corridor,
in the playground.
He was driving me crazy.
"The world's going to end!
The world's going to end!"
He was really getting on my nerves.
"Shut up, Mr Gloom!" I said.
I called him names like 'the Muppet of Doom'.
But he wouldn't stop.
On and on and on he went.
"The world's going to end!"
Finally, I'd had enough.
"Well, then, you won't be needing this," I said.
And I ate his sandwich.
And that was the end of that.

Creative Writing

Today we are going to do creative writing.
We are going to write creatively.
We are to write creatively going.
We going are, creatively, to write.
Write we creatively? Are going to!
Going to write. We are creatively.
Creatively, we to write are going.
To write, going creatively, we are.
Are we to write going? Creatively!
We write creatively (going to are).
Going creatively, we are to write.
To we are write creatively going.
Are we creatively going to? Write!
Today we have done creative writing.

What's in the Box?

In my box there are locks but not a single key.
In my box are pebbles and rocks washed up from a
whispering sea.
In my box are many clocks all set at half past three.

In my box there's an ox, an ibis and a gnu.
In my box are deep-sea docks and a ship sailing into
the blue.
In my box is a set of stocks and tomatoes to throw
at you.

In my box is Fort Knox with all its golden bars.
In my box is a wistful fox gazing upon the stars.
In my box are flocks of sheep playing electric
guitars.

In my box is Goldilocks searching for a place to hide.
In my box is a nasty pox from which many people
have died.
In my box are some stinky socks, so you'd better
not look inside!

Acrostic

A
Cross stick
Rose up
One day
Shouting
Terrible
Insults
Crossly

Fireworks

Fizzing
Iridescence
Raining down sparks,
Exploding!
Whizzing and whirling,
Orange, red, blue, green, yellow,
Rainbows of light,
Kissing the night sky with colour,
Smoking.

Winter

White
Ice frost and snow
No sun after three
Trees scragged black drear
Ears throb red with cold.
Roll on Spring!

Poem in Different Genres

I was on my way to school
when a figure appeared in the air before me.
It was my uncle – or rather it was my uncle's ghost

I was on my way to school
when a car screeched to a halt beside me.
"Get in!" the driver ordered. "The plane leaves for
South America in fifteen minutes."

I was on my way to school
when a small green man with six tentacles and a huge red eye
beckoned me into his spaceship.

I was on my way to school
when my gaze fell on something dull and metallic;
it was a gun and, beyond it, lying half on the path
and half in the bushes, lay a man with a bullet hole
in the middle of his skull.

I was on my way to school
when, from out of the mouth of Merlin's Cave,
a gnome-like creature scampered,
pursued by a huge green dragon, breathing fire.

I was on my way to school
when I saw the girl of my dreams.

I was on my way to school
once upon a time, when I met a cat
wearing a fine pair of leather boots
and a magnificent feathered hat.

I was on my way to school
when I realized I hadn't written my entry for yesterday
and there was so much to report!

I was on my way to school
kicking a stone along the pavement
when Ryan ran up to me.
"Get your kit, Micky!" he gasped.
"You're in the team!"

I was on my way to school
when I heard footsteps on the path behind me
and a low inhuman moan that sent a shiver down my spine.
I turned. There was nothing there, but darkness.

I was on my way to school
with Nursie, when a rider galloped by apace,
discharged his pistol into the air
and proclaimed, "The King hath lost his head!"

I was on my way to school
when suddenly I remembered... it was Sunday!
So I went back home to bed.

Writing in My Shed

Some people do all their writing in their heads,
some people do all their writing in their beds,
some people don't write at all coz they're dead,
but me, I'm Al, I write in a shed.

A library might be the favourite writing place for Ted,
a study is the only place to write for Ned,
a caravan is the preferred scriptorium for Fred.
but me, I'm Al, I write in a shed.

Some people like the cool feel of pencil lead,
some prefer wool or cotton thread,
for others it's glass or concrete or metal instead,
but I'm Al. I like wood. I write in a shed.

Some go to restaurants to be well fed,
some go to church to pray or be wed,
others go to head hunters to get ahead,
but me, I'm Al, I write in a shed.

Some people like to hurtle on a sled
Others like to stuff their cheeks with bread,
Some like to party and paint the town red,
But me, I'm Al, I like to write in my shed.

So if you wonder where I am,
remember what I said
and you'll know where to find me:
I'll be writing in my shed.

Seen Through

"You look good in glasses.
You know, sort of pretty,
brainy too," I said.
"They suit your face,
the shape of your head."
"Yeah, well, you can
get stuffed an' all," she said.

17

On the Beach at New Quay

My brothers ran about playing football,
Mum and Dad spread the picnic rug,
My sister went looking for fossils,
Me, I sat on the sand and dug.

My brothers leapt about with a frisbee,
Mum and Dad had a snooze and a hug,
My sister went poking in rock pools,
Me, I just sat and dug.

My brothers splashed about in the water,
Mum and Dad poured tea from a jug,
My sister climbed a hill of boulders,
Me, I just dug and dug and dug.

My brothers and sisters stopped playing
Mum and Dad started packing away,
But me, in my super sand speedboat,
I sped off across the bay.

Suncream? Who Needs It!

Mum, don't smother me in suncream,
you know I hate that stuff.
You say you're just trying to protect me,
but, Mum, enough is enough.

I look like a freak or a zombie
with my face all white like that,
and now it's in my hair as well
I'm like an albino rat.

You've rubbed it all over my body,
you've covered my arms and my legs,
my elbows look like ping-pong balls,
My knees like hard-boiled eggs.

When I go down to the swimming pool,
I glisten like holographic foil;
I slip and slide though the water
like a chip in a pan of oil.

So, Mum, lay off with that sun stuff,
getting red is just par for the course,
but if you really must smother me in something,
please make it ice-cream and chocolate sauce.

The Lie

"I'm not talking to you," she said.
"You'll just go and put me in one of your poems."
"No, I won't," I said.

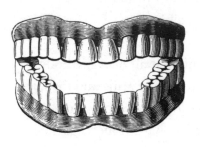

False Impressions

Granny took out her dentures
And sank them in my leg.
"And you thought I was harmless,"
she said.

Turning Ten

I'm doubling my digits,
I'll never see nine again.
I'm moving out of single figures,
coz tomorrow I'll be ten.

I'm leaving behind my boyhood,
and entering the world of men.
I'll probably wake up with a beard
tomorrow, when I'm ten.

This single life is easy,
one number, nice and plain,
but I'm headed for double trouble,
coz tomorrow I'll be ten.

If only time would stand still...
But my wish is all in vain,
cause the clock has just struck midnight.
It's tomorrow, I've just turned ten.

Georgie Porgie

(For my hero George Best)

Georgie Porgie, pudding and pie,
Kissed the girls and made them sigh;
Kissed the ball and made it sing;
Kissed our dreams and made them ring.
Georgie Porgie was our king.

Georgie Porgie whisky and rye,
Kissed the booze to make him high;
Kissed it, kissed it all day long,
Kissed goodbye to ball and song.
Georgie Porgie, what went wrong?

Listen to Your Manager

Be first to the ball! Pass it!
Get it down and play!
Put it out! Clear it!
No, the other way!
Spread out! Take a man!
Come on, get stuck in!
Give it early! Keep it tight!
Knock it down the wing!
Tuck your shirt in! Pull your socks up!
Tie those bloomin' laces!
Wakey, wakey! Get you head up!
You're not at the races!
Hold the line! Don't turn your back!
Turn and face!
Back door! Skills! Roast him!
Use your pace!
Winners! You can do this!
Who are you *marking*?
Peep! The ref's whistle.
At last, the game is starting.

The Carrot Eater

When I was young
my mum used to tell me
that if I ate carrots
I'd be able to see in the dark.
And my dad said
that if I ate carrots
my hair would curl.

So I ate carrots.
I ate lots and lots and lots of carrots.
I ate carrots until they were coming
out of my ears.
Yet my hair is still as straight
as a stalk
and all that I can see in the dark
is darkness.

But I *have* turned bright orange,
so now, when it's dark,
everybody else
can see me.

Song of the Yam

I am a yam
I am, I am!

But I am not
(oh no, oh no!)
I am not a po-ta-to!

Aubergine

There's something about an aubergine,
majestic in its purple skin,
rich and corpulent as a king,
or a baritone about to sing
an aria for an ailing queen,
and jolly up a dreary scene,
and set the sunlight sparkling in
to glory in its glossy sheen.
There's something about an aubergine.

Mango

Come and dance the fruit fandango,
Tongues twist and slide through the tropical tango.
Girl go, boy go, woman go, man go!

Pomegranate

I had a pom-e gran ate,
so now I don't have
one anymore.

Banana

Bendy-bodied
Acid yellow
Now I peel
Away your skin.
Naked you are white
And oh so squidgy sweet!

Fruit Fantasy

They say that what you eat
is what you are,
so if I eat a star fruit
will I be a star?
If I eat a dragon fruit
will I start breathing fire?
If I eat a Kiwi
will I become a flier?
If I eat a papaya
will I become my dad
If I eat bananas
will I go raving mad?
If I eat a prickly pear
will I split into two?
And if I eat an ugli fruit
will I look like you?

Strawberry Madness

At school we get fruit or vegetables
to eat at break time.
Sometimes we get tomatoes or carrots;
sometimes we get apples, satsumas or bananas;
and, sometimes, in the summer, we get strawberries.
We all love it when we get strawberries.
You can hear the murmur go round the class
"Mmm, strawberries!"
But when we get strawberries,
we aren't allowed to eat them at break time;
we have to wait till we come in from play,
because our teacher, Mr Sternum,
has to wash the strawberries.
He washes them in the classroom sink one by one.
It takes him the whole of break time
to wash all those strawberries.

One day I came in from play early
because I wanted to get something from my desk,
a skipping-rope or something,
and I saw Mr Sternum by the sink washing
the strawberries one by one, very slowly, very carefully
like he was washing tiny hearts,
and I asked him why he had to wash all those strawberries,
why we couldn't just eat those strawberries,
without the washing, like the tomatoes and the apples
and the carrots, why?

And Mr Sternum put down the tiny heart-like
strawberries he was washing and he looked at me
and he said that he had to wash all those strawberries,
because unwashed strawberries made you mad.
He'd seen it happen, he said, and strawberry
madness was a terrible thing.
"Oh," I said, because I didn't know about that.
And I asked Mr Sternum what happened when you
had the strawberry madness.
And he said that, well, you might suddenly
start SHOUTING and SHRIEKING
or doing strange things like jumping on other people
or pulling weird faces
or wearing your sweatshirt over your head
or calling your best friend, "Mum".
Things like that, he said.

And I looked out of the window
into the playground and I shook my head.
"Mr Sternum," I said, "I don't think you need
to wash those strawberries. I think it's too late.
I think our whole school has the strawberry madness."
But Mr Sternum just smiled.
That wasn't strawberry madness, he said,
that was the banana madness from the day before.
Banana madness only lasted a day and it wasn't nearly
as bad as the strawberry madness.
And he went back to washing those strawberries
one by one, very slowly, very carefully,
washing the madness away,
into the sink and down the drain,
saving his class from the strawberry madness,
keeping us healthy and sane, he said,
like him.

An Ode to Custard

Custard! Custard! Loverly custard!
Give me custard, thick or thin!
I love its sweet and creamy body.
But most of all I love its skin.

The Chocolate Monster

There's a monster in our house.
She doesn't eat children.
She doesn't suck your blood or grind your bones.
She doesn't do all that nasty stuff that ghouls and
monsters do.
Do you know what she does?
She steals your chocolate and eats it all!
She's the Chocolate Monster.

Now, say your mum bought you a bar
of your favourite chocolate for being very good
and you said, "Thank you", and put the bar on the table
while you went to get a drink. Say that.
Well, when you came back, what would you find?
Nothing, but an empty wrapper, a chocolate skin.
And then you'd know the Chocolate Monster had been!

Say your dad gives your mum a box of chocolates
because he loves her. Say that. It happens.
And your mum gives your dad a big smacking kiss
and then she puts the box of chocolates in the
cupboard.
And, next day, she thinks she'd like one of those chocolates
and she opens up the cupboard and WHAT?!!

The box is empty, all its insides eaten, except
one half-chewed cherry cup. Yuk.
That's right. The Chocolate Monster's been!

The Chocolate Monster loves Christmas ...
but most of all she loves Easter,
because the Chocolate Monster loves Easter eggs.
You can hide them in a tree in the garden.
You can bury them in the earth.
You can cover them with your bedclothes.
You can put them in the most secret place you know.
But the Chocolate Monster will find your chocolate
Easter eggs –
and as sure as eggs are eggs, she'll devour them!

Well, one day I had had enough.
I decided to set a Chocolate Monster trap.
I opened a packet of my favourite chocolate candies –
the ones with lots of different flavoured centres,
like orange, caramel, peanut and honeycomb.
And I took out all the candies except for a few on
the top.
And I filled the rest of the packet with frozen peas instead!
Then I made a hole in the bottom of the packet.

That night, when it was dark as the plainest chocolate,
the Chocolate Monster came and stole my chocolate
candies.
When I woke up, they were gone.

But the Chocolate Monster left a trail behind her,
a trail of frozen peas that had leaked out through the
little hole
I'd made in the candy packet, and I followed the trail...
along the corridor...
   up the stairs ...
     on to the landing ...
       down the stairs again.
(Oh no, that was just a pea I kicked down by mistake.)
Up more stairs ... and up...until I came
to the Chocolate Monster's lair.
Did I dare enter? Did I dare enter the
Chocolate Monster's lair?
I had to. I screwed up my courage and opened the door
and...
Ugh! Eugh! Eek! What a horrible, horrid sight.
The floor was covered in smelly socks and pants,
sweet wrappers, apple cores, empty crisp packets
and other muck.
Yuk!

And there on the bed, in the middle of all that mess,
was the Chocolate Monster!
She was gobbling candies like eyeballs.
She was crunching them like she was grinding bones.
Her face was all bloody with chocolate.
She was eating my chocolate candies!
"Hey, you no-good thieving Chocolate Monster!"
I shouted.
The Chocolate Monster glared at me.
She looked mean and scary.
She had a face so fierce it could make chocolate melt.
She opened her mouth and snarled like she wanted to
eat me!
Then her face changed. It squeezed and squinted.
"Ugh!" she cried and she spat out frozen peas.
Pip, pip, pip, pip... A whole mouthful of frozen peas.
The Chocolate Monster hates frozen peas.
I laughed. "That'll teach you to steal my chocolate," I said.

And do you know what?
The Chocolate Monster learned her lesson.
She never takes my chocolate now.
But sometimes I let her have a little ...
just to keep her sweet!

I Wish I Wish My Family Was Weird

I wish I wish my family was weird,
that my dad had fangs and my mum had a beard.
I wish I wish my family was weird.

If only my dad was a vampire,
he'd hang upside down from the chandelier
and fly out at night
to give the neighbours a fright.
I wish I wish my family was weird.

If only my mum was a mummy,
all bandaged up she'd look funny.
How my friends would grin
at her beard and green skin.
I wish I wish my family was weird.

If only my sister was a ghoul not a girl.
She'd make her eyes fizz and her two heads twirl.
It would be so cool
when we walked into school.
I wish I wish my family was weird.

Imagine if my brother was a werewolf,
from head to foot all hairy and rough.
He'd howl at the moon
and behave like a loon.
I wish I wish my family was weird.

If only my dear gran and grandpa
were aliens who'd come down from Mars.
They'd enthral me for hours
with their incredible powers.
I wish I wish my family was weird.

I wish I wish my family was weird,
that my dad had fangs and my mum had a beard.
I wish I wish my family was weird.

Well, want to know something?
They are!

I Know a Hideous Monster

I know a hideous monster.
It's true, believe me, I do.
He's the ugliest thing I've ever seen
And he smells like doggy poo.

He's got ears like umbrellas
And a nose like a warty stick.
And as for his eyes, I cannot describe them,
If I did it would make you sick.

His tongue is huge and slimy.
His teeth are as black as coal.
His lips are all slobbery and oozing with pus.
He could scare the scariest troll.

His skin is as green as cabbage,
His hair like a brush that's scrubbed the loo.
His neck is covered in sores and boils.
He's hideous through and through.

His arms and legs are stringy,
His body is short and squat.
His toes are hairy, his fingers are fat
And his nails are all crusty with snot.

He grunts and groans like a hippo.
He slithers along like a snake.
If you thought he was cute as a beauty queen,
You'd be making a big mistake!

Yes, I know a hideous monster.
It's true, believe me, I do.
He's the ugliest thing that I've ever seen.
And he looks a lot like ... you!

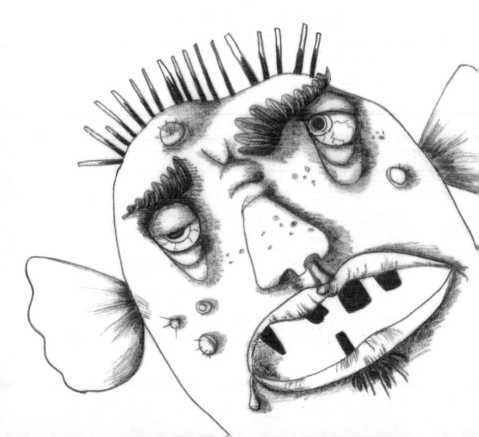

Llawhaden Castle on All Souls Night

On All Souls Night in the drizzling dark,
Gareth and I walked up the muddy path
Past the rest home and the empty car park
To the castle.

Our shoes were filthy and our hair was wet
By the time we passed through the castle gate,
But our spirits were high and our minds set
On our purpose.

I looked about; the walls were steep.
I said, "This is the place they call the keep."
"They can keep it!" cried Gareth with a leap
To the stairway.

We reached the turret that topped the stairs
And entered its gloom as we'd been dared.
I shivered, Gareth sniggered, "Hey, are you scared?"
"Just cold," I said.

Through the window slot the wind moaned in,
Filling the turret with a dirge-like din,
While Gareth's knife scrammed the castle's skin
To carve his name.

It was then I saw it: the faintest gleam,
Like a wavering, failing flashlight beam

That burst suddenly to brightness. Someone screamed.
It was Gareth.

A figure stood where the light had been,
Dressed in robes like a bishop or a king,
And his face was the scariest I'd ever seen
Or ever will.

His eyes were black as a moonless night
Unearthly, inhuman, an awful sight,
That made Gareth and I quiver with fright
And back away.

The figure pointed at us and said,
In a voice so cold we froze in dread,
"You trespass, this place belongs to the dead,
on All Souls Night."

We ran for our lives down the stairs and on,
Stumbling and slipping back the way we'd come,
Through the gates, to where the streetlights shone
And kept running.

We've never returned from that day to this.
And if you visit Llawhaden our advice is:
Be sure to give that old castle a miss
On All Souls Night.

The Dark

There's something moving in the dark tonight,
something huge and slow, just out of my sight;
I hear it sighing and feel like crying,
because I don't know what it is in the dark tonight.

There's something cold about the air tonight;
a shiver, a chill, something not right;
not a ghost or a ghoul, not scary at all,
then why does the air feel so cold tonight?

There's something dying in the dark tonight,
something lovely and sad that won't see dawn's light;
a creature like me that a creature like *me*
has killed and defiled in the dark tonight.

The dark's not outside, it's in me tonight.

The Theme Park After Dark

In the theme park, at night when it's dark,
I've heard it said that's when the dead
assemble inside to ride the rides.
But when they race round Megafobia,
they don't scream, they laugh.
To them, Hydro Water Hell's no more scary
than, say, taking a bath.
They love going up on Vertigo, it doesn't give *them* the frights
(except the headless horseman, who has no head for heights).
The Bounce doesn't make their heart stop,
they don't have one, you see.
And Voodoo Mansion? It's their favourite haunt,
that's where they go for tea!
It's true as they drop down Snake River Falls
their ghostly knuckles are white,
but don't be fooled, that's not from terror,
simply a lack of sunlight.
There's one place, though, in the theme park
that those ghosts and ghouls won't go near.
They never *ever* enter Kidzworld,
for it makes them quake with fear!
All night long they ride the rides
and howl and wail and moan,
then just as the sun begins to rise,
they take the ghost train home.

Letting Her Go

She'd always had baggy skin
but now it was a bag with nothing in.
She was deaf, her fur was grey, she'd flop wherever.
Several times our neighbours brought her home.
Once I rescued her from the road.
"We'd better take her to the vet's," said Dad.
I put her in the basket.
Usually she was wild and scratchy,
but tonight she went in like a mouse.
She was light as a mouse too.
Dad's voice was heavy when we sat in the car,
Puddy on my lap, soundless,
the car engine growling,
"I don't think she'll be coming back."
I nodded, but I hadn't given up.
The vet had saved her before, maybe she would again.

A young cat clinked behind the counter as we waited.
A woman came out of the surgery with two Siamese
cats in a basket.
I smiled. They looked so bright and healthy.
Now it was our turn.
"How is she?" asked the vet and Dad shook his head.
The vet felt Puddy's tummy, smelt her breath,

lifted her in the air. Puddy did nothing.
Last time she'd drawn blood
"You know what I'm going to say," said the vet.
"I think we should let her go, now.
I think we should do that for her."
And then I knew.

She asked me if I wanted to stay and I said I did.
I stroked Puddy and whispered goodbye.
When the needle went in, Puddy crumpled
as if all her air had gone and she slipped away.
Dad bent down and kissed her head.
I kissed her too. Her fur was soft and sort of greasy
like it always was. Then we left,
me holding Puddy's collar, Dad with the empty basket.
It was raining. Dad turned on the engine
but he didn't drive away. He took my hand and
we sat staring out at the windscreen, saying nothing,
watching the wipers wipe away the rain,
watching the rain.

Boy at the Somme

"The last one there is a cow pat!"
grinned the small boy
running between the white headstones
as he began the one hundred metre dash
along the narrow strip of turf separating
Private Tom Atkins, age 18,
of the Lancashire Fusiliers,
from Lieutenant Edward Hollis, age 19,
of the Seaforth Highlanders;
more than twice the distance they managed
over the same small field
that October morning eighty-seven years before
into the spitting venom of the machine guns
that killed them instantly.

Family Plot

Grandma Parsons "fell asleep",
Grandpa Lomax "passed away",
Great Uncle Michael "was called home to rest",
but Davy, our Davy, was hit by a truck
when he ran out to play.

The dead are not really dead,
they live in our hearts, the headstones say.
But my heart is as empty as the other bed,
since Davy, our Davy, was hit by a truck
when he ran out to play.

Summer's Gone

Summer's gone –

just words now in the journal I kept for six blissful weeks
recording the long lingering days out with friends,
flowing from house to
house, game to game, with no rules or routine until
bedtime, sleeping with the sun still one eye opened,
its lazy gaze on my face even through the curtains;

the day we cycled over the downs and gathered caterpillars
in a jar and counted the newts in the old mill house pond
and came across a scampering of wild rabbits in the
tussocky grass
and joked that they were having a game of football;

the jousts with spears of sprouting pampas grass that
we burned
later on the fire at the end of the garden with the old
dining room table
and dad's seatless lion-tamer chair, and toasted marshmallows
in the flames till they were brown and gooey;

the holiday abroad with the thirsty sunshine and the
cool blue pool
to quench it, splashing and shouting and doing seal
tricks on the lilos,
the endless rounds of rummy and uno and fizzy drinks
in bars,
eating strange food from incomprehensible menus -

all gone, ended,
the last page finished, the book shut and put
away, like the shorts and sandals, flippers and goggles,
lie-ins and daytime tv.
Tomorrow it's back to school. Summer's gone,

Autumn's here.

Christmas

"The people who walked in darkness have seen a great light." Isaiah

The people who walked in darkness have seen
giant fairy lights in a multitude of colours,
white lights sparkling in front-garden fir trees,
red lights marking the contours of ivy,
reindeer-pulled sleighs blushing over rooftops,
casinos of lights gushing from housefronts,
merry xmas in neon rashes across the skyline,
santas and snowmen flashing from lampposts,
festive illuminations blinking and glittering on
every high street,
christmas trees twinkling and flickering in every
building,
shop windows glistening like the milky way,
gleaming, glimmering, shimmering, shining...
The people who walked in darkness have seen
great light.

Donkeys and Stars

It's dress rehearsal day for the Nativity,
Reception are trying on their costumes.
There are uniforms draped like skins over desks.
There are donkeys and stars in the classroom.

Jamie has lost his ears and nose.
Ibrahim's tights are all wonky.
Natasha's forgotten her sparkly shoes.
Thomas is pulling the tail off a donkey.

Miss Fowler wants the stars on stage *right now*.
That's Darren and Aaron and Zoe and Jess.
Three of the stars are ready to shine.
Aaron has his head up Mary's dress.

The donkeys are starting their journey,
Carrying their tails so they don't trip over.
They plod their way to the stable scene,
Through a swishing, swirling supernova.

It's dress rehearsal day for the Nativity.
Reception are on stage in their costumes.
There is silence, stillness, a heavenly peace,
Where there were donkeys and stars in the classroom.

Web Warning

Beware!
Somewhere out there
spinning its way across the worldwide web
is a great big enormous
SPIDER
coming to get
you

Scrabble

W₂ A₁ S₁

S₁ C₂ R₁ A₁ B₃ B₃ L₂ E₁

C₂ R₁ E₁ A₁ T₂ D₁

T₂ O₂ A₁ N₁ O₂ Y₁₀

B₃ A₁ D₁

S₁ B₃ E₁ L₂ E₁ R₁ S₁

L₂ K₃ Y₁₀

M₃ E₁ ?

Snow Angel

I lie
down
on the
white ground
slide my arms out, shuffle them up
and down, up and down in the snow like wipers;
now my feet splay too, out in, out in; I stare through
perfectly black-etched trees to a grey
unradiant sky and smile cherubically;
I am power, I am glory,
I can fly on icy wings
I am Gabriel
I am the Archangel
I am ... wet and cold so
it's time to step out of my heavenly body
and join
the snowball fight

instead.

Daybreak

High up in Heaven
a carefree young angel
was spinning light and dark like plates
in the rarefied, celestial air,
when, distracted by a trumpet's call, he fumbled,
lost control,
managed to hold on to dark,
but light slipped away,
dropping through the universe,
spinning through the Earth's orbit
crashing into night, where it broke,
its shattered rays
becoming day.

The Metaphorical Forest

Hedgehog holly, dark green fading
to beige at its prickly edges.

Furry intestines of leafless ivy
entwine the crumbling tree trunks.

Fungi squats on the tree stumps
set out for the squirrels' assembly.

The trees are sleeping dragons,
their grey skin thick and scaly.

The leaves are brown paper fish
swimming across the forest floor.

Amid the mouldering mess of foliage
beats a single yellow heart.

The Heckler

The teacher has a cuddly kitten puppet.
She makes the kitten dance and sing
to cheer up the little girl with the pigtails,
who is crying for her mummy on that first
morning of that very first day.
The little girl stops crying. She smiles.
The teacher says, "Stroke the kitten, Mia, listen to her purr."
"Stroke it, stroke it," chant the children.
The heckler says, "That's not a real kitten.
That's you making it dance. That's you purring.
It's not real."

The teacher hands out the paper and the crayons
and the glue. She holds up a transparent tube,
twinkling with colour.
The teacher says, "Look at the magic dust, children.
You can sprinkle it on your pictures and make
them magical too."
"Ah," sigh the children.
The heckler says, "That's not magic dust. It's just
glitter. You get it in Woolworths."

The teacher picks up a book.
The teacher says, "Now, children. Listen carefully to the story.
I shall be giving out stickers at the end
to the best listeners."
"Stickers!" cry the children. They sit up straight.
They are all ears and eyes.

The heckler says, "I won't be listening to the story.
I won't be getting a sticker. I won't."

The teacher starts to read the story.
The teacher says, "In a wild and windy wood
long ago and far far away there lived a tiny dinosaur
no bigger than a fox but braver than a lion..."
And the heckler says ... nothing.
He listens with his eyes wide and his mouth
slightly open, all wrapt attention
from beginning to end.

The teacher says, "Now, who liked that story
and who would like to hear some more
about that little dinosaur tomorrow?"
"Me! Me! Me!" the children reply in a breathless squeal.
"Not me," says the heckler. "I didn't like that story.
I don't want to hear any more tomorrow."

At the end of the day, the teacher says,
"Tomorrow, we shall have another story.
And play some more games,
And do some more pictures.
Tomorrow we are going to have even more fun!"
"Yes!" shout the children. They wriggle and jump
and clap their hands.
"Not me," says the heckler. "I'm not coming to school
tomorrow. I'm not going to have any fun."

But next morning, guess who's the first one
through the classroom door?

Writing Creatively

Now, class, we're going to do creative writing.
But wait! Before we start to create
there's something we must always do.
Jason? Well done! Write the date.

What's that, Marika? Long date or short?
Excellent question, now let me see...
Well, let's make it the long date,
as today we are writing creatively.

Now I know you're longing to start
and see your words spill out, live,
but there's one thing still missing.
Yes, Holly? Good girl. Objective.

Now today's learning objective is
to create an inspired piece of story-telling.
No, hold on, make that to write
a story with perfect punctuation and spelling.

So there you have it, class.
Now it's time to pick up your pencils and write.
What's that, Thomas? A title? Mmm, something
original and exciting... A Dark and Stormy Night!

Oh, of course, Tanya. Thank you. I'd forgotten.
We have to go to a gym demonstration in the hall.
Pack up, everyone. We'll carry on with this later,
if we've a moment before the end of school.

Haiku

A woman's face floats
like the moon on a silken
sea. "Hi, Koo," I coo.

Welcoming the New Pupils

Good afternoon, boys and girls,
and may I give a special welcome
to all of our new pupils.
Before you start at Marchmont School
I should like to draw your attention to
our disciplinary code.
At Marchmont we operate a series of
ascending cautions, popularly referred to as Cs.
The first of these is a C1.
Should you receive a C1 your name
will be written up on your classroom
whiteboard as a warning.
Should you get a C2, you will have a house point deducted.
A C3 will result in a lunchtime detention;
a C4 an after school detention.
Any pupil receiving a C5 will be removed from
class and made to work in isolation.
The punishment for a pupil guilty of a C6
will be to eat all the scrapings from school dinners
for a week.
For a C7 you will be ordered to clean the school
toilets with your tongue.
For a C8 you will be put in the school stocks and pelted
with rotten fruit, faeces and other matter of a suitably
foul and malodorous nature.

Offenders receiving a C9 will be hung upside down
by the ankles from the school roof for one entire day.
Fir a C10 you will be tied to the back of the
headteacher's car
and dragged for one kilometre through the school grounds.
For a C11 you will have a limb removed
(not your writing hand).
A C12 means execution.
As this is an educational insititution our chosen method
of capital punishment is death by long division
and will be carried out by the Head of Mathematics.
This brings me to the final sanction, C13: exclusion.
I should like to put all of your minds at rest,
however, by pointing out that a C13 has
yet to be given at this school.
Thank you for listening. I hope you enjoy
your time at Marchmont - and live
to tell the tale.

Nursery Rhymes

1.

There was a boy called Louis-Loo,
Who took his mummy to the zoo.
A lion ate her with one bite,
And said, "Thank you, Louis-Loo. Goodnight."

2.

I love custard, I love peas,
I love macaroni cheese.
I love pickles, I love plums.
Put them all inside my tum!

3.

I met a funny author
He was scribbling in his book.
I asked, "What are you writing?"
But he wouldn't let me look.

4.

Hinky-hunky, hankily-dunky
I am a queen, and you are a monkey!

Tic Tac Toe

Tic tac toe,
Your mummy's made of snow.
Your daddy's got a hole in the bottom of his sole
Through which the north wind blows.
Hoo-whee, hoo-whee!
Through which the north wind blows.

Tic tac toe,
Your sister's got a beau.
Your brother saw them snog in a hollowed-out log
And now the whole world knows.
Oh-yay, oh-yay!
And now the whole world knows.

Tic tac toe,
We're putting on a show.
If you don't come, you can kiss my bum.
But now it's time to go.
Farewell, farewell!
For now it's time to go.

Your smile

When you smiled last night
the sun came up.
In less time than it takes
to strike a match or touch a flame
the entire firmament was aglow.
I watched with amazement and delight.
It's not often you see a sunrise at
that time of the day.